MACMILLAN REA
BEGINNER LE

JOHN ESCOTT

Picture Puzzle

MACMILLAN

Founding Editor: John Milne

The Macmillan Readers provide a choice of enjoyable reading materials for learners of English. The series is published at six levels – Starter, Beginner, Elementary, Pre-intermediate, Intermediate and Upper.

Level control
Information, structure and vocabulary are controlled to suit the students' ability at each level.

The number of words at each level:

Starter	about 300 basic words
Beginner	about 600 basic words
Elementary	about 1100 basic words
Pre-intermediate	about 1400 basic words
Intermediate	about 1600 basic words
Upper	about 2200 basic words

Vocabulary
Some difficult words and phrases in this book are important for understanding the story. Some of these words are explained in the story and some are shown in the pictures. From Pre-intermediate level upwards, words are marked with a number like this: ...³. These words are explained in the Glossary at the end of the book.

1

The Girl in the Shopping Mall

It was Friday morning.

'Another boring day at college,' Pete thought. 'Nothing exciting happens to me. I *want* something exciting to happen. I want to meet a beautiful girl.'

It was a fine summer morning. The streets of the big city were busy. Pete did not hurry.

'I want the new story by Stephen King,' he thought. 'I'll get it now.'

He walked into a large shopping mall. There was a big bookshop in the mall. Pete bought the Stephen King book and came out of the shop.

Then something exciting *did* happen!

A girl ran through the crowd of people in the mall. She ran towards Pete. She had short blonde hair and small round glasses. She was very pretty. And she had a camera in her hand. But something was wrong!

Pete looked carefully at the girl's face. 'She's afraid,' he thought. 'Why is she afraid?'

Suddenly, the girl ran up to Pete. She pushed something into his hand!

Pete started to speak. 'Hey! What —?'

But the girl ran away. She disappeared into the crowd.

Pete looked at the thing in his hand. 'This is a film cassette,' he thought. 'Why did she give me this?'

A minute later, Pete saw a man pushing through the crowd. He was a very big man and he was wearing a red shirt. He was in a hurry and he was looking for somebody.

'Is he looking for the girl?' Pete asked himself. 'Or is he looking for a thing, not for a person? Is he looking for a film cassette?'

Pete quickly put the film cassette into his pocket.

The big man's face was angry and worried. He looked at the faces of the people in the mall. He looked carefully at Pete. Then he hurried away.

'That man *is* looking for the girl,' Pete thought. 'Why? She was afraid of him. She gave me the film. Does he want to get the film? This is a puzzle.'

Pete took the cassette out of his pocket and he looked at it again.

'Can I solve the puzzle?' he asked himself. 'I'm going to try to solve it! I want to see the pictures on this film.'

Pete went to a big department store.

An hour later, Pete collected the photos.

Pete went back into the mall and he found a seat. He sat down and he opened the packet of photos. He looked at the six pictures. Three of the photos were pictures of the girl with her friends. Two of the photos were pictures of a young child. The sixth photo was a picture of two men. One of them was tall and thin. In the picture, he was giving the other man a thick brown envelope.

The other man was big. And he was wearing a red shirt!

2

The Story in the Newspaper

Pete looked carefully at the photo. In the picture, the two men were standing in a churchyard. There were some gravestones in the picture. A small part of the church was in the picture too. There was a big tree behind the men. There was a small green gate in a wall, next to the tree. Pete asked himself some questions.

'Where is that church?' he asked himself. 'And who is the tall, thin man? I know the man's face – I'm sure about that. Is he somebody famous?'

'I've seen his picture in a newspaper!' Pete said to himself. 'But *when* did I see it? I must look at some old editions of the *City News*.'

The *City News* was the city's evening newspaper.

Pete looked at the clock in the shopping mall. He had to go to college. But he was worried about the girl. He thought for a few moments. Then he made a decision.

'The girl was frightened about something,' he thought. 'And she's more important than college!'

The *City News* office was on the other side of the city. Pete left the shopping mall and started to walk. He thought about the thick brown envelope in the picture. What was in it? Papers? Money?

'Why did the girl take a photo of the two men?' Pete asked himself. 'And why does the big man want the photo?'

———

Pete arrived at the *City News* office. He went inside the building. There was a table in one corner of a big room. There were four very large books on the table. Inside these books were old editions of the *City News*.

Pete sat down at the table and opened one of the books.

For the next thirty minutes, Pete turned the pages of the *City News*. He looked at every picture in every newspaper.

'Am I wrong?' he thought. 'I can't find —'

And then he *did* find the picture!

The newspaper was nearly two months old. In the picture, the tall thin man was coming out of a large building. Under the picture of the tall thin man, were the words – *Zetter's lawyer, Ronald Thurber.*

'Yes! It's him!' Pete thought.

YESTERDAY IN COURT

Zetter's lawyer, Ronald Thurber.

Yesterday, the court sent Donald Zetter to prison for the murder of James Black. Zetter killed Black in September last year. Black was once a member of Zetter's gang. He gave the police information about Zetter. Two weeks later, Zetter shot Black at Black's home.

The Zetter gang have robbed fourteen banks in the last ten years. And they have killed three people. But now Zetter is in prison.

Pete finished reading about Donald Zetter. He looked at the girl's photo again – the photo of the two men in the churchyard.

'Thurber is Donald Zetter's lawyer,' Pete thought. 'Is the big man a member of Zetter's gang?'

Pete closed the book of newspapers and went out into the street.

'Now I must try to find the girl,' he thought. 'But how am I going to do that?'

3

The Search for the Girl

'First, I must find that churchyard,' Pete thought. He looked again at the photo. He saw part of the church in the picture. But which church was it? He did not know.

'I'll visit all the churches in the city,' he said to himself.

Two hours later, Pete was very tired. He was walking towards St Mark's Church. The church was at the top of a hill, near the city centre.

'Will this be the church in the photo?' Pete thought. 'I've been to eleven churches now, and my feet are painful!'

He walked through some large gates and into the churchyard.

And there was the tree – the tree in the photo! And next to it, there was the wall with the small green gate.

Pete looked at the tree.

'Thurber and the big man stood there together,' thought Pete. 'I'm right – I know that! I have solved the first part of the puzzle!'

There was nobody else in the churchyard. Pete walked up to the church and he opened the heavy door. There was a priest inside the church. He was putting some books on a table. He looked up and he smiled at Pete. He walked towards the young man.

Pete showed the priest the photo.

'Do you know these two men?' he asked.

The priest looked carefully at the photo. Then he spoke. 'No, I'm sorry,' he said. 'I don't know them.'

'Do you know a girl with short blonde hair and small round glasses?' Pete asked. 'She's very pretty.'

The priest smiled again.

'Is she your girlfriend?' he asked.

'No,' Pete replied. 'And I don't know her name. But I saw her this morning. She's afraid of something. I want to help her.'

The priest thought for a moment. 'I *have* seen a girl with blonde hair and round glasses,' he said. 'She walks through the churchyard sometimes. And she *is* very pretty. But I don't know her name. I'm sorry.'

'Thanks for your help,' Pete said.

4

The Big Man

It was lunchtime and Pete was hungry. He wanted something to eat.

There were some shops in the street near the church. One of them sold sandwiches and drinks. Pete went into it. He spoke to the man in the shop.

'A chicken sandwich and a cola, please,' he said.

The man put a sandwich into a paper bag.

'Do you know a girl with blonde hair and small round glasses?' Pete asked him. 'She sometimes walks through the churchyard.'

There was a woman at the back of the shop. She was making sandwiches. Suddenly, she looked up.

'Are you talking about Amy Bates?' the woman asked Pete.

'I don't know the girl's name,' Pete answered.

'Amy has blonde hair, and she wears round glasses,' the woman said. 'She buys bread here sometimes.'

'Does she live near here?' Pete asked.

'She lives in Richfield House, I think,' the woman replied. 'She lives in a flat there. Richfield House is two streets away from here.'

'Thanks,' Pete said.

Pete ate his sandwich and drank his cola. Then he walked to Richfield House.

Richfield House was a large, old building. There were six bell-pushes by the big red door. There was a name next to each bell-push. One of the names was 'Amy Bates'.

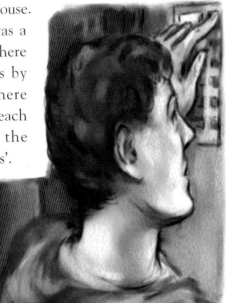

Pete put his finger on the bell-push and rang the bell. Then he waited. There was no answer.

'Hey!' somebody shouted.

Pete looked up and he saw a man. The man was leaning from one of the windows. The window was at the top of the building.

It was the big man!

'Hello,' Pete shouted.

'Are you looking for Amy?' the big man shouted.

For a moment, Pete did not reply. Then he shouted up to the man.

'Yes!'

'Come up to my flat,' the man shouted down. 'I'm waiting for her too.'

Pete heard a sound – BUZZZZ. He pushed the big red door, and it opened. He went inside. He saw some stairs and he started to climb them. Pete climbed up and up! At last, he was on the top floor.

The big man was waiting for him. He stood next to the door of a flat. The door was half open.

'Come in,' the big man said.

Pete and the big man went into the flat. The man shut the door.

'Is this Amy's flat?' Pete asked.

'No,' the big man replied. 'This is *my* flat. But Amy is going to come here soon.'

They walked into a large room. The window was open and Pete heard the cars in the street outside. There were chairs and a table beside the window. In one corner of the room there was a small cooker. Next to that there was a sink. Next to the sink there was a door. The door was closed. Pete looked at the door.

'Is that the door to the bathroom?' he thought.

The big man pulled a chair away from the table.

'Sit down,' he said. 'Amy will be here soon.'

Pete sat down.

'Why do you want to see Amy?' the big man asked.

'I – I've got something for her,' Pete replied.

The big man put his hand into a drawer in the table. A moment later, he took his hand out again.

And now there was a gun in it!

5

Amy

'Amy gave you the film,' the big man said. 'Is that right?'

Pete started to speak. 'No, I —'

'Yes!' the big man shouted suddenly. 'And now you've got the photos. Give them to me!'

Suddenly, Pete heard a noise. He looked at the door next to the sink. 'You've got Amy in there!' he said.

The big man smiled.

'You're right,' he said. 'We were waiting for you. I told Amy, "He'll come. He saw your frightened face. He'll try to find you. He'll try to solve the puzzle. How? He'll get photographs from the film. Then he'll find the churchyard and he'll start asking questions. He'll find this place." Was I right? Did you do all those things?'

Pete did not answer. He looked at the gun.

The big man held out his left hand. 'Give me the photos!' he said.

Pete gave him the packet of photographs. The man opened the packet with one hand. He dropped the photos on the table.

He looked at them. 'Good,' he said. 'Now give me the film. Nobody will make any more photos from that film.'

Slowly, Pete took the film cassette from his pocket.

The big man held out his hand.

'Give me the film!' he shouted.

Suddenly, Pete turned round. He threw the cassette out of the window!

'Hey!' the big man shouted. He ran to the window and he looked down into the street.

There were some people in the street below the window. A woman saw the film cassette and she picked it up.

'That's my film,' the big man shouted down to her. 'I dropped it. Please put it into my letterbox by the front door.'

The man was looking down into the street. He was not looking at Pete. Pete jumped towards him.

The two men fought. Suddenly the big man fired the gun.

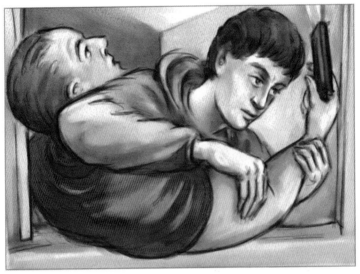

The people in the street heard the sound of the gun.

Hello, police?

Pete pushed the big man. The big man fell to the floor.

Pete moved quickly. The big man fell out of the window.

Pete ran to the bathroom door and opened it.

6
Amy's Story

Two policemen arrived. Amy told the officers her story.

'The big man's name is Wallace,' she said. 'He's a prison officer – he works in the prison in this city. He lives in this flat. I live in another flat in this building.'

'On Tuesday, I saw Wallace talking to a man in the churchyard,' Amy said. 'I knew the other man. I remembered his picture from the *City News*. He's a lawyer. His name is Thurber.'

'We know about Mr Thurber,' one of the policemen said. 'He's Donald Zetter's lawyer. Zetter is in prison, here in the city.'

'And Wallace works at that prison,' Amy said. 'I heard Wallace talking to Thurber. He said, "Bring the money here at nine o'clock on Friday morning. After that, I'll help Zetter." I was worried about his words. Something was wrong – I knew that!'

'What did you do?' Pete asked.

'I went to the churchyard with my camera at nine o'clock this morning,' Amy replied. 'I took a picture of the two men. But Wallace saw me using my camera.'

'What happened next?' Pete asked.

'I ran away, but Wallace ran after me,' Amy replied. 'I ran to the shopping mall. I took the film out of the camera. I wanted to take it to the department store. But I saw Wallace coming near me. I started running again. Then I saw you in the mall.'

'And you gave me the film,' Pete said.

Pete told *his* story to the police officers. Then he asked Amy a question.

'When did Wallace find you?' he asked.

'He was waiting for me outside my flat.' Amy replied. 'He pulled me up the stairs. He pulled me into this flat. And then I told him about you and the film.'

Amy looked at Pete.

'I didn't *want* to tell him about you, but he hit me,' she said quietly. 'After that, he put me in the bathroom and he waited for you.'

29

'I was worried,' Amy said, 'Wallace told me, "The young man is clever. He'll find you. He'll solve the puzzle and he'll come here with the photos." I was very worried about you.'

The police officers started to look for the brown envelope. They found it under Wallace's bed. There was £50,000 inside the envelope.

The policemen, Amy and Pete left the house.

'Does Zetter want to escape from prison?' Pete asked one of the policemen. 'Does he want Wallace to help him? Is the £50,000 for Wallace's help?'

'Yes,' the police officer said. 'We'll talk to Wallace. We'll visit him in hospital later. He'll tell us the truth now – I'm sure about that! Then we'll talk to Ronald Thurber.'

The officer looked at Pete and Amy.

'Thank you,' he said. 'You are clever young people.

Are you friends?'

Pete looked at Amy. Amy looked at Pete.

'We are now!' they said together. And everybody laughed! Then Pete and Amy walked away together.

Published by Macmillan Heinemann ELT
Between Towns Road, Oxford OX4 3PP
Macmillan Heinemann ELT is an imprint of
Macmillan Publishers Limited
Companies and representatives throughout the world
Heinemann is a registered trademark of Harcourt Education, used under licence.

ISBN 1–405072–48–2
EAN 978–1–405072–48–2

Designed by Sue Vaudin
Illustrated by Kieran Phelps
Original cover template design by Jackie Hill
Cover photography by Thom Long/Corbis

Printed in Thailand

2009 2008 2007 2006 2005
10 9 8 7 6 5 4 3 2